Key Stage 2

Addition & Subtraction

Hilary Koll and Steve Mills

Name _____

Schofield & Sims

Introduction

Understanding how addition and subtraction work is as important as knowing when and how to use them. In this book you will learn and practise different ways to add and subtract numbers using both mental and written methods. Trying each method will help you to build a better understanding of what is happening as you add and subtract.

How to use this book

Before you start using this book, write your name in the name box on the first page.

Then decide how to begin. If you want a complete course on addition and subtraction, you should work right through the book from beginning to end. Another way to use the book is to dip into it when you want to find out about a particular topic, such as missing number questions. The Contents page will help you to find the pages you need.

Whichever way you choose, don't try to do too much at once – it's better to work through the book in short bursts.

When you have found the topic you want to study, look out for these icons, which mark different parts of the text.

This icon shows you the activities that you should complete. You write your answers in the spaces provided. You might find it useful to have some spare paper to work on for some of the activities. After you have worked through all the activities on the page, turn to pages 45–49 at the end of the book to check your answers. When you are sure that you understand the topic, put a tick in the box beside it on the Contents page.

On pages 11, 19, 27 and 38 you will find **Progress tests**. These contain questions that will check your understanding of the topics that you have worked through so far. Check your answers on page 50. It is important that you correct any mistakes before moving on to the next section.

On pages 41–44 you will find a **Final test**. This will check your understanding of all the topics. Check your answers on page 51.

Explanation

This text explains the topic and gives examples. Make sure you read it before you start the activities.

This text gives you useful background information about the subject.

Contents

Adding and subtracting

Addition is finding the total of two or more numbers.
Use a plus sign (+) when adding numbers together.

$$3 + 1 = 4$$

Subtraction is really two ideas.
The first is taking away one number from another.
The second is finding the difference between two numbers.

$$4 - 1 = 3$$

Use a minus sign (–) when subtracting numbers.

$$4 \qquad -3 \qquad 1$$

Subtraction is the opposite of addition and addition is
the opposite of subtraction. If you add a number and then
take it away, you are left with the number you started with.

$$6 + 4 - 4 = 6$$

Addition and subtraction words

These words often mean **add**:

| plus | more | sum | total | altogether | increase |

These words often mean **subtract**:

| take | less | minus | left | difference | decrease |

| fewer | take away |

Other useful words to know

Multiples are numbers that are in times tables or beyond.

Multiples of 4 are **4, 8, 12, 16, 20, 24, 28, 32, 36, 40, 44, 48 …** and they carry on and on.

Multiples of 5 are **5, 10, 15, 20, 25, 30, 35, 40, 45, 50, 55 …**
Notice that multiples of **5** end with the unit digit **0** or **5**.

Multiples of 100 are **100, 200, 300, 400, 500 …**
Notice that multiples of **100** end with two zero digits.

Knowing addition and subtraction facts

Explanation

In order to add or subtract large numbers it is important to be able to recall addition and subtraction facts for numbers to **20**. This means remembering the answer without any working out. For example, you probably know that double **5** is **10**. So you know, without any working out, that **5 + 5 = 10** and **10 – 5 = 5**.

Test yourself on this page to see which facts you can answer without working them out. Make a mark next to the facts you still need to learn by heart.

Activities

1 Which of these addition facts can you answer without working out?

a 4 + 4 = _____   b 5 + 3 = _____   c 3 + 6 = _____

d 6 + 9 = _____   e 5 + 7 = _____   f 7 + 6 = _____

g 8 + 4 = _____   h 9 + 8 = _____   i 4 + 7 = _____

2 Which of these subtraction facts can you answer without working out?

a 4 – 3 = _____   b 8 – 3 = _____   c 9 – 4 = _____

d 10 – 2 = _____   e 9 – 7 = _____   f 12 – 6 = _____

g 7 – 4 = _____   h 10 – 3 = _____   i 14 – 7 = _____

3 Which of these addition facts can you answer without working out?

a 14 + 4 = _____   b 11 + 3 = _____   c 12 + 6 = _____

d 9 + 9 = _____   e 12 + 7 = _____   f 13 + 6 = _____

g 15 + 3 = _____   h 14 + 5 = _____   i 11 + 7 = _____

4 Which of these subtraction facts can you answer without working out?

a 18 – 9 = _____   b 16 – 7 = _____   c 13 – 4 = _____

d 14 – 6 = _____   e 15 – 7 = _____   f 13 – 6 = _____

g 17 – 8 = _____   h 13 – 8 = _____   i 14 – 9 = _____

Adding multiples of 5 and 100

Activities

1 Add these multiples of **5**.

a 25 + 15 = _____

b 15 + 35 = _____

c 25 + 45 = _____

d 45 + 35 = _____

e 30 + 55 = _____

f 65 + 25 = _____

g 15 + 75 = _____

h 35 + 60 = _____

i 85 + 10 = _____

2 Fill in the missing numbers.

a 25 + ☐ = 100

b 45 + ☐ = 100

c 65 + ☐ = 100

d 80 + ☐ = 100

e ☐ + 30 = 100

f ☐ + 35 = 100

g ☐ + 15 = 100

h ☐ + 5 = 100

Adding multiples of 100

Multiples of **100** end with **00**. When adding multiples of **100**, think of each number in the question without the **00**.

Example 200 + 800   2 + 8 = 10   200 + 800 = 1000

3 Fill in the missing numbers.

a 400 + 600 = ☐

b 300 + 700 = ☐

c 800 + ☐ = 1000

d 900 + ☐ = 1000

e ☐ + 500 = 1000

f ☐ + 300 = 1000

Adding several numbers

Explanation

When adding several numbers, you can either:

- find pairs that add to **10** and do these first

So with **8 + 5 + 2**, do **8 + 2 + 5 = 15**.

- or start with the largest number first.

So with **3 + 4 + 9**, do **9 + 3 + 4 = 16**.

Activities

1 Find the total for each row and column.

a
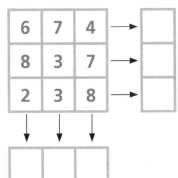

b
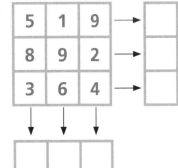

2 Find the total for each row and column.

a

3	9	8	7
4	6	5	12
7	15	5	8
9	11	4	7

b
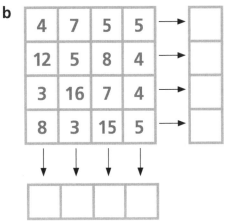

Links between addition and subtraction

Activities

1 Work along each row to find the answers, like this: **10 + 6 − 9 + 3 − 6 + 9 − 3 =** _____

a | **10** — add **6** — subtract **9** — add **3** — subtract **6** — add **9** — subtract **3** = _____

b | **17** — subtract **12** — add **8** — subtract **3** — add **12** — subtract **8** — add **3** = _____

c | **25** — add **16** — subtract **10** — add **5** — subtract **16** — add **10** — subtract **5** = _____

d | **32** — subtract **16** — add **12** — subtract **9** — add **16** — subtract **12** — add **9** = _____

2 What do you notice about each of your answers? Why do you think this is?

_____

_____

_____

3 Use these addition and subtraction facts to help you answer the questions below.

| 31 + 17 = 48 | 29 − 16 = 13 | 23 + 15 = 38 |
| 29 − 17 = 12 | 14 + 28 = 42 | 37 − 28 = 9 |

a 42 − 14 = _____   b 28 + 9 = _____   c 17 + 12 = _____

d 13 + 16 = _____   e 48 − 31 = _____   f 38 − 15 = _____

Adding near doubles

Learning the doubles facts below will make many additions easier to do.

1 + 1 = 2	2 + 2 = 4	3 + 3 = 6	4 + 4 = 8	5 + 5 = 10
6 + 6 = 12	7 + 7 = 14	8 + 8 = 16	9 + 9 = 18	10 + 10 = 20
11 + 11 = 22	12 + 12 = 24	13 + 13 = 26	14 + 14 = 28	15 + 15 = 30
20 + 20 = 40	25 + 25 = 50	30 + 30 = 60	35 + 35 = 70	
40 + 40 = 80	45 + 45 = 90	50 + 50 = 100		

Explanation

When you add numbers that are next to each other, like **6** and **7**, **9** and **10** or **15** and **16**, you can: **double one of the numbers and then add or subtract one.**

Example   6 + 7   →   6 + 6 + 1 = 13   or   7 + 7 − 1 = 13

9 + 10   →   10 + 10 − 1 = 19

15 + 16   →   15 + 15 + 1 = 31

Remember: if you doubled the **higher** number, **subtract** one,
if you doubled the **lower** number, **add** one.

Activities

1   Choose a number from the box. Double your number, then subtract one and add one.

Write your answers on spare paper like this. Do this for all the numbers in the box.

19	34	26	29	47
23	39	43	37	

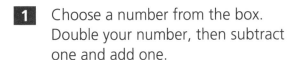

Double 26 = 52   −1 → 51
                 +1 → 53

2   Now use your answers to activity 1 to solve these 'near double' questions.

a   27 + 26 = _____   b   34 + 35 = _____   c   23 + 24 = _____

d   19 + 18 = _____   e   38 + 37 = _____   f   44 + 43 = _____

g   39 + 38 = _____   h   47 + 48 = _____   i   29 + 30 = _____

j   270 + 260 = _____   k   340 + 350 = _____   l   380 + 370 = _____

m   440 + 430 = _____   n   180 + 190 = _____   o   470 + 460 = _____

Patterns in calculations

Explanation

If you know one number fact, then you can use it to work out others.
We can look for patterns in calculations.

Example If you know that $\qquad$ **16 + 3 = 19**
you can work out that $\qquad$ **16 + 13 = 29** and **16 + 23 = 39**

Example If you know that $\qquad$ **5 + 10 = 15**
you can work out that $\qquad$ **5 + 100 = 105** and **5 + 1000 = 1005**

Activities

1 Look for patterns to help you answer these questions. Work down the columns.

a **23 + 5 = _____**

   33 + 5 = _____

   43 + 5 = _____

   53 + 5 = _____

b **17 + 18 = _____**

   17 + 28 = _____

   17 + 38 = _____

   17 + 48 = _____

c **26 – 15 = _____**

   36 – 15 = _____

   46 – 15 = _____

   56 – 15 = _____

d **3 + 6 = _____**

   30 + 60 = _____

   300 + 600 = _____

   3000 + 6000 = _____

e **8 + 7 = _____**

   80 + 70 = _____

   800 + 700 = _____

   8000 + 7000 = _____

f **10 – 6 = _____**

   100 – 6 = _____

   1000 – 6 = _____

   10 000 – 6 = _____

2 Look for patterns to help you fill in the missing numbers.

a

+	1	2	3	4
1	2	3	4	5
2	3		5	
3	4	5		
4			7	

b

+	6	8	10	12
4	10	12	14	
7	13	15		
10			20	
13	19			

Addition & Subtraction

Progress test 1

1 Fill in the missing numbers.

a 30 + ☐ = 100

b 15 + ☐ = 100

c ☐ + 40 = 100

d ☐ + 55 = 100

e 300 + ☐ = 1000

f 600 + ☐ = 1000

2 Add these numbers.

a $6 + 8 + 4 =$ _____

b $3 + 9 + 6 =$ _____

c $7 + 2 + 8 + 12 =$ _____

d $4 + 14 + 6 + 11 =$ _____

3 Use these addition and subtraction facts to help you answer the questions below.

$36 + 19 = 55$ $38 - 17 = 21$ $29 + 14 = 43$

a $21 + 17 =$ _____

b $43 - 14 =$ _____

c $55 - 36 =$ _____

4 Add these numbers.

a $29 + 28 =$ _____

b $37 + 38 =$ _____

c $43 + 44 =$ _____

d $420 + 410 =$ _____

e $380 + 390 =$ _____

f $480 + 470 =$ _____

5 Look for patterns to help you answer these questions.

a $26 + 5 =$ _____

$36 + 5 =$ _____

$46 + 5 =$ _____

$56 + 5 =$ _____

b $19 + 17 =$ _____

$19 + 27 =$ _____

$19 + 37 =$ _____

$19 + 47 =$ _____

c $9 + 7 =$ _____

$90 + 70 =$ _____

$900 + 700 =$ _____

$9000 + 7000 =$ _____

Partitioning

Splitting numbers up makes adding them easier. This is called **partitioning**.

- Split the numbers into tens and units.

- Add the tens.

- Add the units.

- Add the two answers together.

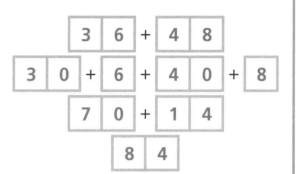

Activities

1 Use the diagrams to add these numbers.

a
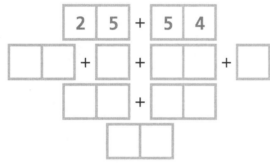

b
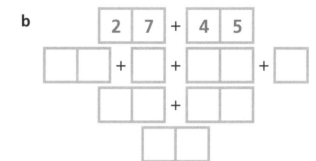

c
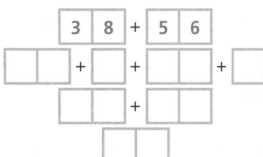

d
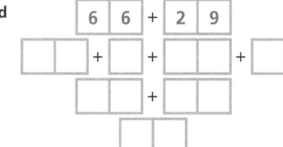

e
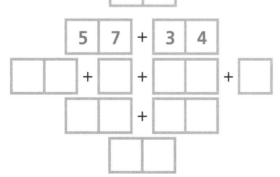

f

2 Try these, using a similar method, in your head.

   a 24 + 58 = _____   **b** 38 + 27 = _____   **c** 27 + 62 = _____

   d 39 + 46 = _____   **e** 43 + 48 = _____   **f** 73 + 18 = _____

Adding near multiples

Explanation

Adding near multiples of 10

To add numbers that are close to multiples of **10**, like **59** or **48**, add the multiple of **10** and adjust afterwards.

Example 59 + 36 → 60 + 36 = 96 → subtract **1** → 95

56 + 31 → 56 + 30 = 86 → add **1** → 87

48 + 45 → 50 + 45 = 95 → subtract **2** → 93

Think carefully about whether you need to adjust by adding or subtracting.

Activities

1 Add these numbers.

a   47 + 19 = _____   b   35 +   9 = _____   c   53 + 29 = _____

d   63 + 21 = _____   e   19 + 74 = _____   f   57 + 32 = _____

g   11 + 125 = _____   h 236 + 19 = _____   i 354 + 21 = _____

j 474 + 31 = _____   k   49 + 527 = _____   l 615 + 52 = _____

Adding near multiples of 100

You can use this method to add numbers that are close to multiples of **100**.

Example 439 + 99 → 439 + 100 = 539 → subtract **1** → 538

103 + 567 → 100 + 567 = 667 → add **3** → 670

Think carefully about whether you need to adjust by adding or subtracting.

2 Add these numbers.

a 236 + 99 = _____   b 362 + 99 = _____   c 475 + 99 = _____

d 346 + 101 = _____   e 101 + 384 = _____   f 475 + 102 = _____

g 378 + 199 = _____   h 537 + 199 = _____   i 198 + 624 = _____

j 647 + 201 = _____   k 201 + 764 = _____   l 865 + 202 = _____

Adding hundreds, tens and ones

Explanation

When adding hundreds, tens or ones to 3-digit numbers, remember to use what you know about place value.

For the 3-digit number **436** there are **4 hundreds**, **3 tens** and **6 ones** (or units).

Look at how the digits change when we add hundreds, tens or ones.

Example 436 + 300 = 736   436 + 50 = 486   436 + 2 = 438

Activities

1 Use your knowledge of place value to help you answer these questions.

a 474 + 200 = _____   b 525 + 50 = _____

c 832 + 40 = _____   d 852 + 7 = _____

e 462 + 400 = _____   f 225 + 60 = _____

g 936 + 50 = _____   h 247 + 2 = _____

i 654 + 200 = _____   j 953 + 40 = _____

When adding hundreds, tens or ones you sometimes count across a hundreds or tens boundary, so more than one digit of the answer will be changed.

Example 267 + 60

267 + 60 = 327

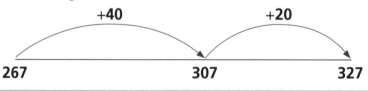

2 Answer these additions involving counting across a boundary.

a 474 + 50 = _____   b 585 + 50 = _____

c 882 + 40 = _____   d 352 + 70 = _____

e 423 + 9 = _____   f 225 + 6 = _____

g 938 + 5 = _____   h 247 + 7 = _____

i 654 + 80 = _____   j 653 + 50 = _____

Addition & Subtraction

Subtracting hundreds, tens and ones

Explanation

When subtracting hundreds, tens or ones from 3-digit numbers, remember to use what you know about place value.

For the 3-digit number **874** there are **8 hundreds**, **7 tens** and **4 ones** (or units).

Look at how the digits change when we subtract hundreds, tens or ones.

Example 874 – 300 = 574   874 – 50 = 824   874 – 2 = 872

Activities

1 Use place value ideas to help you answer these questions.

a 474 – 200 = _____   **b** 585 – 50 = _____

c 872 – 40 = _____   **d** 859 – 7 = _____

e 762 – 400 = _____   **f** 295 – 60 = _____

g 966 – 50 = _____   **h** 247 – 2 = _____

i 654 – 200 = _____   **j** 943 – 40 = _____

When subtracting hundreds, tens or ones you sometimes count back across a hundreds or tens boundary so more than one digit of the answer will be changed.

Example 738 – 60

738 – 60 = 678

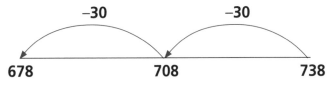

2 Answer these subtractions involving counting back across a boundary.

a 444 – 50 = _____   **b** 515 – 20 = _____

c 812 – 40 = _____   **d** 352 – 70 = _____

e 423 – 9 = _____   **f** 225 – 6 = _____

g 931 – 5 = _____   **h** 246 – 7 = _____

i 654 – 80 = _____   **j** 753 – 90 = _____

Finding small differences

Explanation

You can find the difference between numbers by counting on.

Example Find the difference between **58** and **64**.

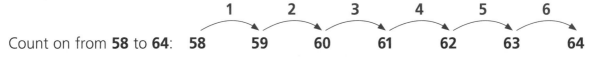

Count on from **58** to **64**: 58 59 60 61 62 63 64

The difference between **58** and **64** is **6**.

You can also use a blank number line, with **60** as a 'stepping stone'.

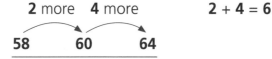

2 more **4** more **2 + 4 = 6**

58 60 64

Activities

1 Find the difference between these numbers by counting on.

a **19** and **25** _____

b **48** and **54** _____

c **67** and **73** _____

d **78** and **86** _____

e **85** and **96** _____

f **97** and **104** _____

2 Answer these questions by counting on.

a **103 − 97 =** _____

b **206 − 198 =** _____

c **304 − 296 =** _____

d **404 − 395 =** _____

e **407 − 396 =** _____

f **503 − 492 =** _____

3 Use the blank number lines to find these differences.

a **406 − 394 =** _____

394 _____ 406

b **805 − 793 =** _____

793 _____ 805

c **1006 − 998 =** _____

d **2005 − 1997 =** _____

e **3004 − 2993 =** _____

f **4008 − 3992 =** _____

Subtracting near multiples

Explanation

Subtracting near multiples of 10

To subtract numbers that are close to multiples of **10**, like **39** or **68**, subtract the multiple of **10** and adjust afterwards.

Example $64 - 19$ → $64 - 20 = 44$ → add 1 → 45

$87 - 31$ → $87 - 30 = 57$ → subtract 1 → 56

Think carefully about whether you need to adjust by adding or subtracting.

Activities

1   Subtract these numbers.

a $54 - 9 =$ _____

b $63 - 19 =$ _____

c $67 - 29 =$ _____

d $74 - 21 =$ _____

e $86 - 21 =$ _____

f $95 - 32 =$ _____

g $127 - 19 =$ _____

h $243 - 19 =$ _____

i $354 - 42 =$ _____

j $584 - 52 =$ _____

k $675 - 39 =$ _____

l $774 - 59 =$ _____

Subtracting near multiples of 100

You can use this method to subtract numbers that are close to multiples of **100**.

Example $547 - 98$ → $547 - 100 = 447$ →   add 2   →   449

$675 - 103$ → $675 - 100 = 575$ →   subtract 3   →   572

Think carefully about whether you need to adjust by adding or subtracting.

2   Subtract these numbers.

a $236 - 99 =$ _____

b $264 - 99 =$ _____

c $345 - 99 =$ _____

d $367 - 101 =$ _____

e $375 - 101 =$ _____

f $453 - 102 =$ _____

g $477 - 199 =$ _____

h $653 - 299 =$ _____

i $695 - 202 =$ _____

j $734 - 302 =$ _____

k $825 - 298 =$ _____

l $783 - 397 =$ _____

Written methods of addition using partitioning

When numbers get too large to work with in your head, you will need a method for working on paper. When adding any numbers on paper, make sure you line the columns up correctly and approximate first. The method below uses partitioning to split up the numbers. Start by adding the hundreds, then the tens and then the units.

Example 326 + 471

```
  H T U        (Approx. 300 + 500 = 800)
  3 2 6
+ 4 7 1
  ─────
  7 0 0        (300 + 400)
    9 0        (20 + 70)
      7        (6 + 1)
  ─────
  7 9 7
```

Activities

1 Use partitioning to add these numbers.

a 352 + 36 = _____

b 426 + 63 = _____

c 517 + 72 = _____

d 428 + 151 = _____

e 534 + 245 = _____

f 316 + 483 = _____

g 647 + 232 = _____

h 718 + 281 = _____

i 603 + 396 = _____

Written addition with carrying

This sum has some carrying. You can either start with the hundreds or the units.   **637 + 285**

Example

Either:
```
  H T U
  6 3 7      (Approx. 600 + 300 = 900)
+ 2 8 5
  ─────
  8 0 0      (600 + 200)
  1 1 0      (30 + 80)
    1 2      (7 + 5)
  ─────
  9 2 2
```

Or:
```
  H T U
  6 3 7
+ 2 8 5
  ─────
    1 2      (7 + 5)
  1 1 0      (30 + 80)
  8 0 0      (600 + 200)
  ─────
  9 2 2
```

2 Use partitioning to add these numbers.

a 427 + 46 = _____

b 572 + 75 = _____

c 438 + 94 = _____

d 634 + 287 = _____

e 229 + 484 = _____

f 673 + 169 = _____

g 123 + 798 = _____

h 503 + 399 = _____

i 375 + 487 = _____

Addition & Subtraction

Progress test 2

1 Use the diagrams to add these numbers:

a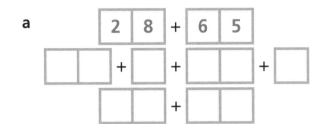

b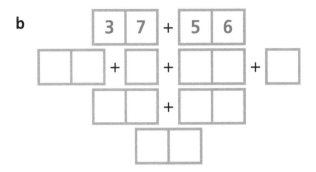

2 Find the difference between these numbers by counting on.

a **39** and **46** _____

b **57** and **65** _____

c **305 – 296 =** _____

d **604 – 592 =** _____

3 Use the blank number lines to find these differences.

a **507 – 495 =** _____

b **706 – 694 =** _____

_____

_____

4 Add these numbers.

a **56 + 9 =** _____

b **47 + 19 =** _____

c **59 + 46 =** _____

d **364 + 131 =** _____

e **59 + 536 =** _____

f **477 + 89 =** _____

5 Subtract these numbers.

a **73 – 9 =** _____

b **87 – 19 =** _____

c **64 – 28 =** _____

d **365 – 199 =** _____

e **587 – 201 =** _____

f **672 – 298 =** _____

6 Use partitioning to add these numbers.

a **433 + 36 =** _____

b **456 + 183 =** _____

c **378 + 563 =** _____

Written addition of 3-digit numbers

When you feel confident with partitioning, you can shorten the method.

Example $326 + 471$

```
  H T U
  3 2 6
+ 4 7 1
  7 9 7
```

(Approx. $300 + 500 = 800$)

This calculation has no carrying.

Activities

1 Use this shorter method or one of your own to add these numbers.

a $452 + 26 = $ _____

b $356 + 22 = $ _____

c $417 + 51 = $ _____

d $318 + 261 = $ _____

e $424 + 165 = $ _____

f $516 + 263 = $ _____

g $557 + 231 = $ _____

h $617 + 261 = $ _____

i $506 + 392 = $ _____

Written addition with carrying

Example $568 + 274$ *(Approx. $550 + 300 = 850$)*

This calculation has lots of carrying so it is best to start with the units.
Follow the boxes if you're not sure.

```
  H T U
  5 6 8
+ 2 7 4
  8 4 2
  1 1
```

start here

| $5 + 2 + 1 = 8$ Write **8**. | ← | $6 + 7 + 1 = 14$ Write **4** and carry **1** hundred into the hundreds column. | ← | $8 + 4 = 12$ Write **2** and carry **1** ten into the tens column. |

2 Use this method or one of your own to add these numbers.

a $372 + 29 = $ _____

b $485 + 53 = $ _____

c $537 + 82 = $ _____

d $367 + 268 = $ _____

e $573 + 189 = $ _____

f $547 + 386 = $ _____

g $658 + 194 = $ _____

h $509 + 394 = $ _____

i $689 + 278 = $ _____

Addition & Subtraction

Written subtraction using partitioning

Written subtraction using partitioning

When subtracting large numbers on paper, make sure you line the columns up correctly and approximate first.

Example 746 – 432

H	T	U
7	4	6
– 4	3	2
3	1	4

→ *(Approx. 700 – 400 = 300)*

$700 + 40 + 6$
$– 400 + 30 + 2$
$300 + 10 + 4 = 314$

Check your answer by **adding** the last two rows: **432 + 314 = 746**

Activities

1 Use partitioning to subtract these numbers.

a 475 – 53 = _____

b 568 – 47 = _____

c 589 – 76 = _____

d 538 – 223 = _____

e 569 – 356 = _____

f 746 – 525 = _____

g 683 – 461 = _____

h 858 – 745 = _____

i 963 – 621 = _____

Written subtraction with exchanges

Example 637 – 275   *(Approx. 600 – 300 = 300)*

This calculation needs exchanges. Follow the arrows to see how these happen.

H	T	U
6	3	7
– 2	7	5

→

$600 + 30 + 7$
$– 200 + 70 + 5$

→

$500 + 130 + 7$
$– 200 + 70 + 5$
$300 + 60 + 2 = 362$

Notice that we have changed **600 + 30** into **500 + 130**.
This makes it easier to subtract the **70** in **275**.

2 Use this method or one of your own to subtract these numbers.

a 385 – 57 = _____

b 428 – 46 = _____

c 463 – 92 = _____

d 472 – 284 = _____

e 564 – 376 = _____

f 741 – 584 = _____

g 623 – 367 = _____

h 753 – 696 = _____

i 964 – 689 = _____

Written subtraction of 3-digit numbers

Written subtraction

When you feel confident with partitioning, you can shorten the method.

Example 647 − 432

```
  H  T  U          (Approx. 600 − 400 = 200)
  6  4  7
− 4  3  2
  _____
  2  1  5          This calculation has no exchange.
```

Check your answer by **adding** the last two rows: **432 + 215 = 647**

Activities

1 Use this shorter method or one of your own to subtract these numbers.

a 578 − 63 = _____ b 484 − 73 = _____ c 689 − 57 = _____

d 658 − 236 = _____ e 669 − 457 = _____ f 693 − 472 = _____

g 656 − 423 = _____ h 845 − 724 = _____ i 989 − 676 = _____

Written subtraction with exchanges

This calculation needs exchanges. Follow the boxes if you're not sure.

Example 642 − 275   (Approx. 600 − 300 = 300)

```
    H    T    U
    ₆5   ₄¹3  ¹2
−   2    7    5
    _____
    3    6    7
```

← ———————————————————————————————— start here

| 5 − 2 = 3 Write 3 in the hundreds column. | ← | 3 − 7 we can't do, so change 1 of the hundreds into 10 tens. The 3 becomes 13 tens. Take 7 from 13. Write 6 in the tens column. | ← | 2 − 5 we can't do, so change 1 of the tens into 10 units. Cross out a ten, leaving 3 tens. The 2 becomes 12 units. Take 5 from 12. Write 7 in the units column. |

2 Use this method or one of your own to subtract these numbers.

a 625 − 53 = _____ b 453 − 47 = _____ c 685 − 94 = _____

d 473 − 396 = _____ e 463 − 376 = _____ f 628 − 459 = _____

g 637 − 568 = _____ h 832 − 545 = _____ i 917 − 628 = _____

Addition & Subtraction

Written addition of 4-digit numbers

Explanation

Written addition with carrying

Once you feel confident adding 3-digit numbers using the written column method, you can add 4-digit numbers in the same way.

Example 6846 + 3358   *(Approx. 7000 + 3000 = 10 000)*

This calculation has lots of carrying, so follow the boxes if you're not sure.

	TTh	Th	H	T	U
		6	8	4	6
+		3	3	5	8
	1	0	2	0	4
		1	1	1	1

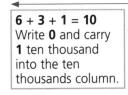
6 + 3 + 1 = 10
Write **0** and carry **1** ten thousand into the ten thousands column.

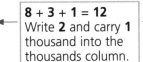
8 + 3 + 1 = 12
Write **2** and carry **1** thousand into the thousands column.

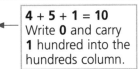
4 + 5 + 1 = 10
Write **0** and carry **1** hundred into the hundreds column.

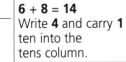
6 + 8 = 14
Write **4** and carry **1** ten into the tens column.

Activities

1 Use this method or one of your own to add these numbers.

a

	TTh	Th	H	T	U
		5	6	2	8
+		3	5	9	1

b

	TTh	Th	H	T	U
		6	8	3	6
+		3	6	5	6

c

	Th	H	T	U
	7	7	3	8
+	7	2	5	2

d

	Th	H	T	U
	5	7	2	8
+	5	5	2	2

e

	Th	H	T	U
	5	7	2	6
+	8	2	5	3

f

	Th	H	T	U
	1	9	4	6
+	4	7	2	1

g

	Th	H	T	U
	5	7	3	9
+	8	9	5	5

h

	Th	H	T	U
	7	9	6	9
+	5	6	8	5

Written addition of 4- and 5-digit numbers

Explanation

This calculation has lots of carrying, so follow the boxes if you're not sure.

Example 46 538 + 25 907   *(Approx. 45 000 + 25 000 = 70 000)*

TTh	Th	H	T	U
4	6	5	3	8
+ 2	5	9	0	7
7	2	4	4	5
1	1		1	

| **4 + 2 + 1 = 7** Write **7** in the ten thousands column. | **6 + 5 + 1 = 12** Write **2** and carry **1** ten thousand. | **5 + 9 = 14** Write **4** and carry **1** thousand into the thousands column. | **3 + 0 + 1 = 4** Write **4** in the tens column. | **8 + 7 = 15** Write **5** and carry **1** ten into the tens column. |

Activities

1 Use this method or one of your own to add these numbers.

a 42 323 +   2376 = _____

b 5356 + 23 235 = _____

c 34 815 +   5462 = _____

d 53 729 + 45 347 = _____

e 28 693 + 41 521 = _____

f 38 938 + 27 237 = _____

2 Here is a list of the number of people who went to the cinema to watch two different films in April.

Week	On Cranbrook Hill	Frozen Sun
1	37 687	42 809
2	56 709	69 871
3	35 092	78 278
4	19 486	92 004

How many people in total:

a saw *On Cranbrook Hill* in weeks **1** and **2**? _____

b saw *Frozen Sun* in weeks **1** and **2**? _____

c saw *On Cranbrook Hill* in weeks **3** and **4**? _____

d saw *Frozen Sun* in weeks **3** and **4**? _____

e went to the cinema in week **1**? _____

f went to the cinema in week **4**? _____

Addition & Subtraction

Explanation

Once you feel confident subtracting 3-digit numbers using the written column method, you can subtract 4-digit numbers in the same way.

Example 7653 − 4716   *(Approx. **8000 − 5000 = 3000**)*

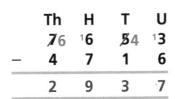

```
      Th    H     T     U
      ⁷6   ¹6    ⁵4    ¹3
  −    4    7     1     6
      ─────────────────────
       2    9     3     ⁷7
```

6 − 4 = 2
Write **2** in the thousands column.

6 − 7 doesn't work, so change **1** thousand into **10** hundreds. Cross out **1** of the thousands. Take **7** from **16**. Write **9** in the hundreds column.

4 − 1 = 3
Write **3** in the tens column.

3 − 6 doesn't work, so change **1** ten into **10** units. Cross out **1** of the tens. The **3** becomes **13**. Take **6** from **13**. Write **7** in the units column.

Activities

1   Use this method or one of your own to subtract these numbers.

a
```
   Th  H  T  U
    5  2  8  7
 −  3  5  3  1
   ───────────
```

b
```
   Th  H  T  U
    6  8  3  6
 −  3  6  5  6
   ───────────
```

c
```
    7  7  3  8
 −  4  2  5  2
   ───────────
```

d
```
    5  2  8  1
 −  4  7  2  6
   ───────────
```

e
```
    8  2  8  4
 −  7  9  7  8
   ───────────
```

f
```
    9  2  1  5
 −  6  4  6  3
   ───────────
```

g
```
    9  1  5  3
 −  8  2  7  6
   ───────────
```

h
```
    9  6  3  3
 −  7  7  4  8
   ───────────
```

i
```
    7  3  5  2
 −  4  9  5  5
   ───────────
```

j
```
    9  6  6  4
 −  5  9  7  8
   ───────────
```

Written subtraction of 4- and 5-digit numbers

Explanation

This calculation needs several exchanges. Follow the boxes if you're not sure.

Example 75 634 − 43 716   *(Approx. **70 000** − **40 000** = **30 000**)*

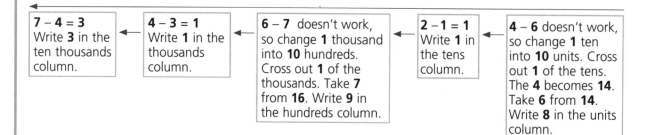

| 7 − 4 = 3 Write **3** in the ten thousands column. | 4 − 3 = 1 Write **1** in the thousands column. | 6 − 7 doesn't work, so change **1** thousand into **10** hundreds. Cross out **1** of the thousands. Take **7** from **16**. Write **9** in the hundreds column. | 2 − 1 = 1 Write **1** in the tens column. | 4 − 6 doesn't work, so change **1** ten into **10** units. Cross out **1** of the tens. The **4** becomes **14**. Take **6** from **14**. Write **8** in the units column. |

Activities

1 Use this method or one of your own to subtract these numbers.

a 37 867 − 2345 = _____

b 45 756 − 34 574 = _____

c 54 914 − 39 462 = _____

d 63 629 − 45 784 = _____

e 66 251 − 57 648 = _____

f 71 452 − 38 974 = _____

2 Here is a list of attendances at some football matches.

Match **1**	Liverpool v Arsenal	**46 829**
Match **2**	Birmingham v Everton	**37 054**
Match **3**	Man United v Spurs	**67 649**
Match **4**	Newcastle U v Bolton W	**52 346**
Match **5**	Aston Villa v Chelsea	**49 903**
Match **6**	Blackburn R v Southampton	**23 485**

Find the difference between the attendances at these matches:

a Match **1** and Match **4**   _____

b Match **2** and Match **6**   _____

c Match **3** and Match **5**   _____

d Match **4** and Match **6**   _____

e Match **3** and Match **6**   _____

f Match **5** and Match **4**   _____

Addition & Subtraction

Progress test 3

1 Use a written method to add these 3-digit numbers.

    a 528 + 391 = _____

    b 462 + 474 = _____

    c 628 + 357 = _____

    d 486 + 856 = _____

2 Use a written method to subtract these 3-digit numbers.

    a 828 − 478 = _____

    b 915 − 663 = _____

    c 924 − 688 = _____

    d 803 − 577 = _____

3 Use a written method to add these 4-digit numbers.

    a 5228 + 3591 = _____

    b 4836 + 3616 = _____

    c 4675 + 8591 = _____

    d 6767 + 6556 = _____

4 Use a written method to subtract these 4-digit numbers.

    a 8324 − 3118 = _____

    b 9145 − 6623 = _____

    c 5253 − 2563 = _____

    d 8531 − 6678 = _____

5 Use a written method to add these 5-digit numbers.

    a 53 628 + 33 556 = _____

    b 63 836 + 7656 = _____

    c 62 573 + 63 683 = _____

    d 91 573 + 63 556 = _____

6 Use a written method to subtract these 5-digit numbers.

    a 84 328 − 51 678 = _____

    b 33 145 − 9676 = _____

    c 57 573 − 38 467 = _____

    d 93 105 − 6987 = _____

Using rounding and inverses to check

Activities

1 First write an approximation for each of these additions or subtractions underneath it.

a 4875 + 3195 = _____

_____ + _____ = _____

b 6836 – 3656 = _____

_____ – _____ = _____

c 8943 – 4052 = _____

_____ – _____ = _____

d 3281 + 4726 = _____

_____ + _____ = _____

e 6428 + 4591 = _____

_____ + _____ = _____

f 8267 – 3158 = _____

_____ – _____ = _____

2 Now answer each of the calculations in activity **1**.

3 Check each answer by doing an inverse calculation. Write the calculations below.

a _____

b _____

c _____

d _____

e _____

f _____

Missing number questions

Explanation

When finding missing numbers, think about which number in the question will be the largest. This can help you decide whether to use addition or subtraction to find the missing number.

$3267 + \boxed{} = 6943$

$6943 - 3267 = 3676$

In this addition, the answer (**6943**) will be the largest number, so the missing number must be smaller. You can use the **inverse** operation (subtraction) here to find it.

So the missing number is **3676**.

$7452 - \boxed{} = 4637$

$7452 - 4637 = 2815$

In this subtraction, the first number (**7452**) will be the largest number, so the missing number must be smaller. You use subtraction here to find it.

So the missing number is **2815**.

$\boxed{} - 3624 = 5132$

$5132 + 3624 = 8756$

In this subtraction, the first number (the missing one) will be the largest number. You need to use the inverse operation (addition) here to find it.

So the missing number is **8756**.

Activities

1 Find each missing number.

a $6894 - \boxed{} = 2564$

b $2845 + \boxed{} = 6894$

c $\boxed{} + 3563 = 4637$

d $\boxed{} - 1856 = 5533$

e $7452 - \boxed{} = 2845$

f $3451 + \boxed{} = 6942$

g $\boxed{} + 2562 = 7321$

h $\boxed{} - 6734 = 2244$

Adding more than two numbers

Explanation

You can add as many numbers as you like, as long as you line up the numbers so that each digit is in the correct column. Make sure the units all line up correctly.

Example 586 + 3154 + 472 + 2837   *(Approx. **600 + 3000 + 500 + 3000 = 7100**)*

Th	H	T	U
	5	8	6
3	1	5	4
	4	7	2
+ 2	8	3	7
7	0	4	9
	2	2	1

Look for pairs of digits that add to **10**, such as **7** and **3** or **6** and **4**, etc.

Activities

1 Add these numbers, approximating first.

a 257 + 32 + 86

Approximation:

H	T	U
2	5	7
	3	2
+	8	6

b 37 + 203 + 553

Approximation:

H	T	U
	3	7
2	0	3
+ 5	5	3

c 627 + 1476 + 278

Approximation:

Th	H	T	U
	6	2	7
1	4	7	6
+	2	7	8

2 Approximate first, then line up the numbers and find the total.

a 2746 + 475 + 164

Approximation:

Th	H	T	U
2	7	4	6
+			

b 456 + 2785 + 4324

Approximation:

Th	H	T	U
+			

c 5786 + 442 + 954

Approximation:

Th	H	T	U
+			

Addition & Subtraction

Understanding very large numbers

Explanation

It is important to know the value of digits in large numbers when adding and subtracting. This chart shows the number two million, two hundred and twenty-two thousand, two hundred and twenty-two which is written as **2 222 222**.

Millions	Hundred thousands	Ten thousands	Thousands	Hundreds	Tens	Units
2	2	2	2	2	2	2
↓	↓	↓	↓	↓	↓	↓
2 000 000 +	200 000 +	20 000 +	2000 +	200 +	20 +	2

Activities

1   Write the value of the digit **8** in each number.

a   **48 424** _____   b   **738 952** _____

c   **8 315 664** _____   d   **114 823** _____

e   **2 871 249** _____   f   **2 789 045** _____

2   Write these numbers in figures.

a   three million, six hundred and twelve thousand, one hundred and sixteen _____

b   four million, one hundred and ten thousand, eight hundred and four _____

c   one million, twelve thousand and fifty-five _____

3   Answer these additions.

a   **300 000 + 40 000 + 3000 + 200 + 50 + 2 =** _____

b   **5 000 000 + 400 000 + 2000 + 6 =** _____

c   **4 000 000 + 40 000 + 500 + 80 + 4 =** _____

d   **300 000 + 3000 + 40 + 1 =** _____

Using place value ideas to add and subtract

Explanation

Some additions and subtractions, even of large numbers, can be solved in your head, using ideas of place value.

Example

153 132 + 21 006

= 174 138

> Look at each digit in the number being added: **21 006**
> Increase the ten thousands digit by **2**
> Increase the thousands digit by **1**
> Increase the units digit by **6**

1 784 758 − 103 020

= 1 681 738

> Look at the number being subtracted: **103 020**
> Decrease the hundred thousands digit by **1**
> Decrease the thousands digit by **3**
> Decrease the tens digit by **2**

Activities

1 Answer these additions using place value ideas.

a   565 248 + 101 001 = _____

b   452 857 + 21 040 = _____

c   424 113 + 33 040 = _____

d   356 254 + 203 005 = _____

e   1 565 144 + 303 002 = _____

f   244 463 + 1 101 000 = _____

g   352 023 + 204 500 = _____

h   1 436 225 + 1 020 001 = _____

2 Answer these subtractions using place value ideas.

a   565 248 − 33 001 = _____

b   452 857 − 201 040 = _____

c   1 866 232 − 101 001 = _____

d   662 893 − 401 003 = _____

e   3 905 335 − 1 303 005 = _____

f   573 785 − 50 022 = _____

g   5 565 248 − 320 040 = _____

h   1 363 825 − 301 800 = _____

Written addition of decimals and money

Explanation

You can add decimals and money in the same way that you add whole numbers. Make sure you line up the decimal points.

Example

58.6 + 31.2

```
  T  U . t     (Approx.
  5  8 . 6      59 + 31 = 90)
+ 3  1 . 2
  8  9 . 8
```

£15.74 + £23.87

```
  T  U . t  h    (Approx.
  1  5 . 7  4     £16 + £24 = £40)
+ 2  3 . 8  7
  3  9 . 6  1  →  £39.61
       1     1
```

When you are adding decimals it is very important to get an approximate answer first to make sure the decimal point is in the right place.

Activities

1   Add these numbers.

a
```
  2  5 . 7
+ 1  3 . 2
```

b
```
  3  6 . 6
+ 2  5 . 3
```

c
```
  4  5 . 7
+ 2  7 . 8
```

d
```
  5  3 . 6  5
+ 3  6 . 8  4
```

e
```
  6  2 . 0  8
+ 2  7 . 9  5
```

f
```
  7  4 . 9  2
+ 1  6 . 4  9
```

2   Add these amounts of money.

a
```
  £ 3 6.7 1
+ £ 2 4.2 6
```

b
```
  £ 4 5.6 7
+ £ 3 5.3 8
```

c
```
  £ 5 5.4 7
+ £ 2 7.8 2
```

d
```
  £ 6 3.8 5
+ £ 2 6.7 4
```

e
```
  £ 7 2.5 8
+ £ 1 7.9 5
```

f
```
  £ 7 4.9 7
+ £ 2 6.4 6
```

Written subtraction of decimals and money

Explanation

You can subtract decimals and money in the same way that you subtract whole numbers. Make sure you line up the decimal points.

76.8 – 54.3

T	U	.	t	*(Approx.*
7	6	.	8	*77 – 54 = 23)*
– 5	4	.	3	
2	2	.	5	

£47.58 – £21.79

T	U	.	t	h	*(Approx.*
4	7	.	5	8	*£48 – £22 = £26)*
– 2	1	.	7	9	
2	5	.	7	9	→ £25.79

Check your answers by **adding** the bottom two lines of the calculations.

Activities

1 Subtract these numbers.

a
```
    3  6 . 7
 -  1  5 . 2
 _____
```

b
```
    3  8 . 6
 -  1  9 . 3
 _____
```

c
```
    4  5 . 6
 -  2  8 . 8
 _____
```

d
```
    5  6 . 7  5
 -  3  9 . 8  4
 _____
```

e
```
    6  2 . 1  9
 -  4  7 . 8  8
 _____
```

f
```
    7  2 . 7  5
 -  6  6 . 8  9
 _____
```

2 Subtract these amounts of money.

a
```
  £  4  7 . 7  2
 -£  2  4 . 3  1
 _____
```

b
```
  £  5  3 . 2  7
 -£  3  2 . 3  8
 _____
```

c
```
  £  5  8 . 4  3
 -£  3  7 . 8  1
 _____
```

d
```
  £  6  9 . 2  3
 -£  6  3 . 4  5
 _____
```

e
```
  £  7  6 . 1  8
 -£  6  7 . 6  9
 _____
```

f
```
  £  9  5 . 0  1
 -£  7  8 . 9  9
 _____
```

Addition and subtraction of decimals

When adding or subtracting decimals with different numbers of digits, and using a written method, be careful to line up the digits carefully. You might also need to write in extra zeros to make subtractions easier, so that the numbers have the same number of decimal places.

Example 25.35 − 3.712 = 25.350 − 3.712

T	U	.	t	h	th
2	⁵4̸.		¹3	⁵4̸	¹0
−			3 . 7	1	2
2	1	.	6	3	8

Activities

1   Set these questions out in columns and answer them using a written method.

a   **1.58 + 21.485 =** _____

b   **46.646 − 4.132** _____

c   **2.583 + 35.5 =** _____

d   **46.6 − 7.37 =** _____

e   **52.6 + 3.584 =** _____

f   **63.8 − 9.573 =** _____

Word problems 1

Activities

1 **9543** people visited the Coliseum cinema this year.
This was **2704** more than last year.
How many people visited the cinema last year?

_____

2 Josh buys a bag of crisps for **39**p, a drink for **34**p and a magazine for £**1.69**. How much change does he get from £**5**?

_____

3 A car park has **12 785** spaces. **9598** spaces are empty.
How many cars are in the car park?

_____

4 Ella has £**235.24** in her bank account. She withdraws £**50** in cash and pays £**58.74** with her debit card. How much is left in her account after these two transactions?

_____

5 Chandini is going on a trip. She is allowed three bags that weigh up to **27**kg in total. She has one bag that weighs **14**kg and another that weighs $7\frac{1}{2}$kg. What is the maximum that the third bag can hold?

_____

Addition & Subtraction

Word problems 2

When solving addition and subtraction problems that include larger numbers, it is helpful to check whether these can be easily solved in your head using place value.

Example Amelia had £**5398** and paid £**1070** for a new TV. She was also given £**1400** for selling her car. How much money has she now?

Th	H	T	U
5	3	9	8	– 1 0 7 0
4	3	2	8	+ 1 4 0 0

Decrease the thousands digit by **1** and the tens digit by **7**

Increase the thousands digit by **1** and the hundreds digit by **4**

£ 5 7 2 8

Activities

1 Answer these problems mentally.

a Two TVs are for sale. One costs £**402** more than the other. If the cheaper TV costs £**526**, what does the more expensive one cost? _____

b There were **4627** men and **2020** women at a rugby match. How many adults were there altogether? _____

c A male elephant is **3735**mm tall. A female elephant is **602**mm shorter. How tall is she? _____

d Three local schools raise money for charity. St Paul's raises £**232**, Hawsker raises £**204** and Honeywell raises £**360**. How much more than £**500** have they raised in total? _____

2 You can answer some of these problems mentally but you may need to use another method for others.

a In **1999** Beata was **38** years old. In which year was she born? _____

b In **2011** Oliver was **45** years old. In which year was he born? _____

c Matt has £**4645** in a bank account. He pays in £**378** more. How much more than £**5000** has he now? _____

d There were **3243** men, **3150** women and **1203** children at a concert. How many people were there altogether? _____

Progress test 4

1 Find each missing number.

a $5748 - \boxed{} = 1564$

b $3627 + \boxed{} = 9564$

c $\boxed{} + 1536 = 4443$

d $\boxed{} - 1427 = 8523$

2 Find these totals.

a $6894 + 463 + 2536 + 108 =$ _____

b $353 + 46 + 4563 + 1022 =$ _____

3 Answer these additions.

a $600\,000 + 40\,000 + 3000 + 300 + 50 + 2 =$ _____

b $2\,000\,000 + 500\,000 + 2000 + 6 =$ _____

c $3\,000\,000 + 40\,000 + 500 + 70 + 4 =$ _____

4 Answer these additions using place value ideas.

a $465\,246 + 102\,001 =$ _____

b $821\,857 + 21\,030 =$ _____

c $926\,113 + 33\,040 =$ _____

d $563\,254 + 203\,005 =$ _____

5 Add these amounts of money.

a
```
  £ 4 6 . 7 5
+ £ 2 8 . 2 6
─────────────
```

b
```
  £ 4 6 . 6 5
+ £ 3 5 . 2 8
─────────────
```

c
```
  £ 5 5 . 7 6
+ £ 2 7 . 8 4
─────────────
```

6 Subtract these amounts of money.

a
```
  £ 3 6 . 7 1
− £ 1 3 . 2 6
─────────────
```

b
```
  £ 4 8 . 6 7
− £ 3 5 . 3 9
─────────────
```

c
```
  £ 4 3 . 0 7
− £ 2 7 . 6 2
─────────────
```

Addition & Subtraction

Word problems 3

Explanation

Some word problems involve two or more steps. Read the question carefully and take each step at a time.

Example James earns **£2368** for completing a building job. He pays **£486** of this amount in tax and puts the rest into his bank account. There was **£1947** in his bank account before he paid the money in. How much is there in the bank account now?

Use subtraction to find how much he pays into the bank.	**2368 − 486 = 1882**
Then use addition to find how much is in the account now.	**1947 + 1882 = 3829**
Remember to check your answer and write it using the correct unit.	**£3829**

Activities

1 Answer these problems.

a Emily has **£48.63** in her wallet and **£74.85** in her bank account. She uses her money to buy a computer game that costs **£101.49**. How much money does she have now? _____

b A famous footballer earned **£7 654 743** in one year. In the following year he earned **£944 354** more. How much did he earn in the two years put together? _____

c Li's Gran is **67** years old. Li's mum is **39** years younger than Li's Gran and Li is four times as young as her mum. Li's older brother is **6** years older than Li. How old is Li's older brother? _____

d Sarah buys a bag of apples weighing **1200**g, a **986**g pineapple and two tins of beans weighing **507**g each. Find the total mass of her shopping and write how many grams less than **4**kg it is. _____

e Jasper buys items costing **£13.74**, **£17.37** and **£48.67** and the shop gives him an **£8** discount. He pays with **£100** in cash. How much change is he given? _____

f Alfie's grandad was born in **1965**. Alfie was born in **2004** when Alfie's mum was **20** years old. How old was Alfie's grandad when Alfie's mum was born? _____

Word problems 4

Explanation

Watch out for when a variety of units are used together in a word problem. First change them so that they are the same unit.

Example Peter cuts a piece of string into three lengths. One is **4.5**cm long, one is **3.15**m long and the third is **0.3**m long. How long was the string before it was cut?

Change the measurements all to centimetres and add them.

4.5cm + **3.15**m + **0.3**m
      ↓   ↓
4.5cm + **315**cm + **30**cm = **349.5**cm

Remember to write the correct unit in your answer.

Activities

1 Solve these problems.

a Sam joins four lengths of wood together, end-to-end.
One is **17.5**cm long, one is **0.42**m long, one is **1.1**m
long and the fourth is **13**cm long. How long is that altogether? _____

b I have three bags of sweets. One weighs **250**g, one weighs
1.1kg and the third weighs **275.5**g. How much do they
weigh altogether? _____

c Kim weighs two suitcases ready for a flight. One suitcase
weighs **20.7**kg, another weighs **1500**g less than this.
What is the total weight of the suitcases? _____

d Lucy ran **5.7**km on Monday and **9300**m on Tuesday.
How much further did she run on Tuesday than on Monday? _____

e Jacob, Charlie and Ava each have full drinks bottles.
Jacob's bottle contains **330**ml, Ava's bottle contains **0.5**l
and Charlie's bottle contains $\frac{1}{4}$ of a litre. How much do
they have altogether? _____

f A lorry driver travels **164**km in the morning, stops for lunch,
and then travels **17500**m in the afternoon before reaching
his destination. How much further than **180**km did he
travel in total? _____

Addition & Subtraction

Final test

1   Fill in the missing numbers.

a   35 + ☐ = 100   b 700 + ☐ = 1000   c ☐ + 100 = 1000

2   Add these numbers.

a   4 + 8 + 6 = _____   b 13 + 9 + 7 + 4 = _____

3   Use these addition and subtraction facts to help you answer the questions below.

45 + 19 = 64	54 − 18 = 36	38 + 17 = 55

a 55 − 17 = _____   b 36 + 18 = _____   c   64 − 45 = _____

4   Add these numbers.

a 29 + 27 = _____   b 370 + 380 = _____   c 480 + 490 = _____

5   Find the difference between these numbers by counting on.

a **39** and **46** _____   b **708** and **691** _____

6   Add these numbers.

a 77 + 29 = _____   b 365 + 119 = _____   c 273 + 498 = _____

7   Subtract these numbers.

a 63 − 29 = _____   b 683 − 199 = _____   c 361 − 98 = _____

8 Use partitioning to add these numbers. Show your working in the space provided.

a **527 + 56 =** _____

b **653 + 287 =** _____

9 Add these numbers.

a **372 + 25 =** _____

b **436 + 53 =** _____

c **473 + 265 =** _____

d **568 + 479 =** _____

10 Subtract these numbers.

a **475 − 53 =** _____

b **587 − 46 =** _____

c **724 − 386 =** _____

d **841 − 593 =** _____

11 Add these numbers.

a **53 347 + 3432 =** _____

b **6326 + 43 675 =** _____

12 Write an approximation for this addition and this subtraction and then calculate each answer.

a **2847 + 6195 =** _____

b **9884 − 2193 =** _____

_____ + _____ = _____

_____ − _____ = _____

c Check your answers using an inverse calculation. Write the calculations you used here.

_____

_____

13 Subtract these numbers.

a 46 859 – 4347 = _____

b 54 217 – 28 574 = _____

14 Add these numbers.

a 28 + 835 + 167 = _____

b 3207 + 2059 + 331 + 83 = _____

15 Answer these questions.

a
```
    2   6 . 7   4
  + 1   2 . 2   8
  _____

  _____
```

b
```
    £ 2   7 . 7   3
  + £ 3   4 . 5   6
  _____

  _____
```

16 Answer these questions.

a
```
    3   7 . 7   5
  - 1   8 . 8   4
  _____

  _____
```

b
```
    £ 5   3 . 5   6
  - £ 4   7 . 6   2
  _____

  _____
```

17 Find each missing number.

a 4789 − ☐ = 1957

b 3657 + ☐ = 6894

c ☐ + 6432 = 9648

d ☐ − 1753 = 973

18 Answer these questions.

a
```
    £ 4   6 . 3   2
  - £ 1   9 . 0   4
  _____

  _____
```

b
```
    £ 7   1 . 4   3
  + £ 2   3 . 8   9
  _____

  _____
```

19 Answer these questions using place value ideas.

a   565 248 +   203 001 = _____   b   652 857 + 21 040 = _____

c 2 905 335 − 1 303 005 = _____   d   573 766 − 50 022 = _____

e   424 113 +   53 040 = _____   f 1 662 893 − 401 003 = _____

20 Solve this problem.

12 948 people visited the Atlas theme park this year.

This was **3861** less than last year.

How many people visited the theme park last year?   _____

21 Set these questions out in columns and answer them using a written method.

a **11.5 + 3.594 =**   _____

b **46.66 − 4.843 =**   _____

22 Solve these problems.

a Jackie weighs two suitcases ready for a flight. One suitcase
weighs **23.6**kg, another weighs **1700**g less than this.
What is the total weight of the suitcases?   _____

b Noah cuts a piece of ribbon into three lengths. One is
9.5cm long, one is **1.75**m long and the third is **0.5**m long.
How long was the string before it was cut?   _____

Answers to Activities

Page 5: Knowing addition and subtraction facts

1
a 8	**b** 8	**c** 9
d 15	**e** 12	**f** 13
g 12	**h** 17	**i** 11

2
a 1	**b** 5	**c** 5
d 8	**e** 2	**f** 6
g 3	**h** 7	**i** 7

3
a 18	**b** 14	**c** 18
d 18	**e** 19	**f** 19
g 18	**h** 19	**i** 18

4
a 9	**b** 9	**c** 9
d 8	**e** 8	**f** 7
g 9	**h** 5	**i** 5

Page 6: Adding multiples of 5 and 100

1
a 40	**b** 50	**c** 70
d 80	**e** 85	**f** 90
g 90	**h** 95	**i** 95

2
a 75	**b** 55
c 35	**d** 20
e 70	**f** 65
g 85	**h** 95

3
a 1000	**b** 1000
c 200	**d** 100
e 500	**f** 700

Page 7: Adding several numbers

1 **a**   **b**

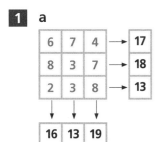

2 **a**   **b**

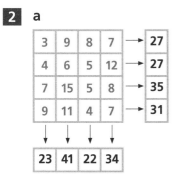
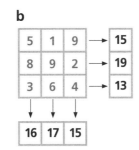
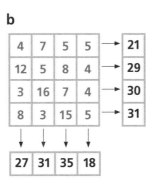

Page 8: Links between addition and subtraction

1 **a** 10 **b** 17 **c** 25 **d** 32

2 For each addition there is a similar subtraction that undoes it and for each subtraction there is a similar addition that undoes it.

3
a 28	**b** 37	**c** 29
d 29	**e** 17	**f** 23

Page 9: Adding near doubles

1 Answers on spare paper in any order.

Number	Double	−1	+1
19	38	37	39
34	68	67	69
26	42	51	53
29	58	57	59
47	94	93	95
23	46	45	47
39	78	77	79
43	86	85	87
37	74	73	75

2
a 53	**b** 69	**c** 47
d 37	**e** 75	**f** 87
g 77	**h** 95	**i** 59
j 530	**k** 690	**l** 750
m 870	**n** 370	**o** 930

Page 10: Patterns in calculations

1
a 28, 38, 48, 58
b 35, 45, 55, 65
c 11, 21, 31, 41
d 9, 90, 900, 9000
e 15, 150, 1500, 15 000
f 4, 94, 994, 9994

2 **a**

+	1	2	3	4
1	2	3	4	5
2	3	4	5	6
3	4	5	6	7
4	5	6	7	8

b

+	6	8	10	12
4	10	12	14	16
7	13	15	17	19
10	16	18	20	22
13	19	21	23	25

Answers to Activities continued

Page 12: Partitioning

1

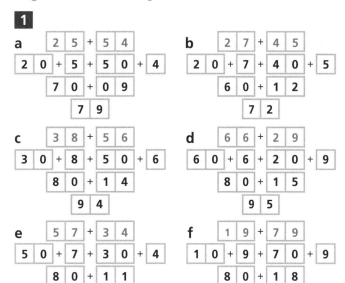

a 25 + 54
20 + 5 + 50 + 4
70 + 09
79

b 27 + 45
20 + 7 + 40 + 5
60 + 12
72

c 38 + 56
30 + 8 + 50 + 6
80 + 14
94

d 66 + 29
60 + 6 + 20 + 9
80 + 15
95

e 57 + 34
50 + 7 + 30 + 4
80 + 11
91

f 19 + 79
10 + 9 + 70 + 9
80 + 18
98

2 **a** 82   **b** 65   **c** 89
d 85   **e** 91   **f** 91

Page 13: Adding near multiples

1 **a** 66   **b** 44   **c** 82
d 84   **e** 93   **f** 89
g 136   **h** 255   **i** 375
j 505   **k** 576   **l** 667

2 **a** 335   **b** 461   **c** 574
d 447   **e** 485   **f** 577
g 577   **h** 736   **i** 822
j 848   **k** 965   **l** 1067

Page 14: Adding hundreds, tens and ones

1 **a** 674   **b** 575
c 872   **d** 859
e 862   **f** 285
g 986   **h** 249
i 854   **j** 993

2 **a** 524   **b** 635
c 922   **d** 422
e 432   **f** 231
g 943   **h** 254
i 734   **j** 703

Page 15: Subtracting hundreds, tens and ones

1 **a** 274   **b** 535
c 832   **d** 852
e 362   **f** 235
g 916   **h** 245
i 454   **j** 903

2 **a** 394   **b** 495
c 772   **d** 282
e 414   **f** 219
g 926   **h** 239
i 574   **j** 663

Page 16: Finding small differences

1 **a** 6   **b** 6   **c** 6
d 8   **e** 11   **f** 7

2 **a** 6   **b** 8   **c** 8
d 9   **e** 11   **f** 11

3 **a** 12   **b** 12
c 8   **d** 8
e 11   **f** 16

Page 17: Subtracting near multiples

1 **a** 45   **b** 44   **c** 38
d 53   **e** 65   **f** 63
g 108   **h** 224   **i** 312
j 532   **k** 636   **l** 715

2 **a** 137   **b** 165   **c** 246
d 266   **e** 274   **f** 351
g 278   **h** 354   **i** 493
j 432   **k** 527   **l** 386

Addition & Subtraction

Page 18: Written methods of addition using partitioning

1
a 388	**b** 489	**c** 589
d 579	**e** 779	**f** 799
g 879	**h** 999	**i** 999

2
a 473	**b** 647	**c** 532
d 921	**e** 713	**f** 842
g 921	**h** 902	**i** 862

Page 20: Written addition of 3-digit numbers

1
a 478	**b** 378	**c** 468
d 579	**e** 589	**f** 779
g 788	**h** 878	**i** 898

2
a 401	**b** 538	**c** 619
d 635	**e** 762	**f** 933
g 852	**h** 903	**i** 967

Page 21: Written subtraction using partitioning

1
a 422	**b** 521	**c** 513
d 315	**e** 213	**f** 221
g 222	**h** 113	**i** 342

2
a 328	**b** 382	**c** 371
d 188	**e** 188	**f** 157
g 256	**h** 57	**i** 275

Page 22: Written subtraction of 3-digit numbers

1
a 515	**b** 411	**c** 632
d 422	**e** 212	**f** 221
g 233	**h** 121	**i** 313

2
a 572	**b** 406	**c** 591
d 77	**e** 87	**f** 169
g 69	**h** 287	**i** 289

Page 23: Written addition of 4-digit numbers

1
a 9219	**b** 10492
c 14990	**d** 11250
e 13979	**f** 6667
g 14694	**h** 13654

Page 24: Written addition of 4- and 5-digit numbers

1
a 44699	**b** 28591
c 40277	**d** 99076
e 70214	**f** 66175

2
- **a** 94396
- **b** 112680
- **c** 54578
- **d** 170282
- **e** 80496
- **f** 111490

Page 25: Written subtraction of 4-digit numbers

1
a 1756	**b** 3180
c 3486	**d** 555
e 306	**f** 2752
g 877	**h** 1885
i 2397	**j** 3686

Page 26: Written subtraction of 4- and 5-digit numbers

1
a 35522	**b** 11182
c 15452	**d** 17845
e 8603	**f** 32478

2
- **a** 5517
- **b** 13569
- **c** 17746
- **d** 28861
- **e** 44164
- **f** 2443

Answers to Activities continued

Page 28: Using rounding and inverses to check

1
  a 5000 + 3000 = 8000
  b 7000 – 4000 = 3000
  c 9000 – 4000 = 5000
  d 3000 + 5000 = 8000
  e 6000 + 5000 = 11000
  f 8000 – 3000 = 5000

2
  a 8070
  b 3180
  c 4891
  d 8007
  e 11019
  f 5109

3 These are example answers.
  a 8070 – 3195
  b 3180 + 3656
  c 4891 + 4052
  d 8007 – 4726
  e 11019 – 4591
  f 5109 + 3158

Page 29: Missing number questions

1
  a 4330   b 4049
  c 1074   d 7389
  e 4607   f 3491
  g 4759   h 8978

Page 30: Adding more than two numbers

1
  a 375   b 793   c 2381

2
  a 3385   b 7565   c 7182

Page 31: Understanding very large numbers

1
  a 8000 or 8 thousand
  b 8000 or 8 thousand
  c 8000000 or 8 million
  d 800 or 8 hundred
  e 800000 or 8 hundred thousand
  f 80000 or 80 thousand

2
  a 3612116
  b 4110804
  c 1012055

3
  a 343252
  b 5402006
  c 4040584
  d 303041

Page 32: Using place value ideas to add and subtract

1
  a 666249   b 473897
  c 457153   d 559259
  e 1868146   f 1345463
  g 556523   h 2456226

2
  a 532247   b 251817
  c 1765231   d 261890
  e 2602330   f 523763
  g 5245208   h 1062025

Page 33: Written addition of decimals and money

1
  a 38.9   b 61.9   c 73.5
  d 90.49   e 90.03   f 91.41

2
  a £60.97   b £81.05   c £83.29
  d £90.59   e £90.53   f £101.43

Answers to Activities continued

Page 34: Written subtraction of decimals and money

1 **a** 21.5 **b** 19.3

    c 16.8 **d** 16.91

    e 14.31 **f** 5.86

2 **a** £23.41 **b** £20.89

    c £20.62 **d** £5.78

    e £8.49 **f** £16.02

Page 35: Addition and subtraction of decimals

1 **a** 23.065 **b** 42.514 **c** 38.083

    d 39.23 **e** 56.184 **f** 54.227

Page 36: Word problems 1

1 6839

2 £2.58

3 3187

4 £126.50

5 5.5kg

Page 37: Word problems 2

1 **a** £928

    b 6647

    c 3133mm

    d £296

2 **a** 1961 **b** 1966

    c £23 **d** 7596

Page 39: Word problems 3

1 **a** £21.99 **b** £16 253 840

    c 13 years old **d** 800g

    e £28.22 **f** 19 years old

Page 40: Word problems 4

1 These are example answers.

    a 182.5cm

    b 1625.5g

    c 39.9kg or 39 900g

    d 3.6km or 3600m

    e 1080ml or 1.08l

    f 1.5km

Answers to Progress tests

PROGRESS TEST 1 – Page 11

1 a 70   b 85
    c 60   d 45
    e 700   f 400

2 a 18   b 18
    c 29   d 35

3 a 38   b 29   c 19

4 a 57   b 75   c 87
    d 830   e 770   f 950

5 a 31, 41, 51, 61
    b 36, 46, 56, 66
    c 16, 160, 1600, 16 000

PROGRESS TEST 2 – Page 19

1 a   b

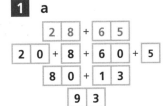

2 a 7   b 8
    c 9   d 12

3 a 12   b 12

4 a 65   b 66   c 105
    d 495   e 595   f 566

5 a 64   b 68   c 36
    d 166   e 386   f 374

6 a 469   b 639   c 941

PROGRESS TEST 3 – Page 27

1 a 919   b 936
    c 985   d 1342

2 a 350   b 252
    c 236   d 226

3 a 8819   b 8452
    c 13 266   d 13 323

4 a 5206   b 2522
    c 2690   d 1853

5 a 87 184   b 71 492
    c 126 256   d 155 129

6 a 32 650   b 23 469
    c 19 106   d 86 118

PROGRESS TEST 4 – Page 38

1 a 4184   b 5937
    c 2907   d 9950

2 a 10 001
    b 5984

3 a 643 352
    b 2 502 006
    c 3 040 574

4 a 567 247   b 842 887
    c 959 153   d 766 259

5 a £75.01   b £81.93   c £83.60

6 a £23.45   b £13.28   c £15.45

Addition & Subtraction

Answers to Final test

FINAL TEST – Pages 41–44

1 **a** 65 **b** 300 **c** 900

2 **a** 18 **b** 33

3 **a** 38 **b** 54 **c** 19

4 **a** 56 **b** 750 **c** 970

5 **a** 7 **b** 17

6 **a** 106 **b** 484 **c** 771

7 **a** 34 **b** 484 **c** 263

8 **a** 583 **b** 940

9 **a** 397 **b** 489
   c 738 **d** 1047

10 **a** 422 **b** 541
   c 338 **d** 248

11 **a** 56 779 **b** 50 001

12 These are example answers.
   a 3000 + 6000 = 9000, 9042
   b 10 000 − 2000 = 8000, 7691
   c 9042 − 6195, 7691 + 2193

13 **a** 42 512 **b** 25 643

14 **a** 1030 **b** 5680

15 **a** 39.02 **b** £62.29

16 **a** 18.91 **b** £5.94

17 **a** 2832 **b** 3237
   c 3216 **d** 2726

18 **a** £27.28 **b** 95.32

19 **a** 768 249 **b** 673 897
   c 1 602 330 **d** 523 744
   e 477 153 **f** 1 261 890

20 16 809

21 **a** 15.094 **b** 41.817

22 These are example answers.
   a 45.5 kg or 45 500 g
   b 234.5 cm